Insertion of ps

Anice Holanda Nunes Maia

Insertion of psychology students in the hospital

Systematization and standard operating procedures for internships

ScienciaScripts

This book is a translation from the original published under ISBN 978-620-2-17277-6.

Publisher:
Sciencia Scripts
is a trademark of
Dodo Books Indian Ocean Ltd. and OmniScriptum S.R.L publishing group

120 High Road, East Finchley, London, N2 9ED, United Kingdom
Str. Armeneasca 28/1, office 1, Chisinau MD-2012, Republic of Moldova, Europe

ISBN: 978-620-7-23049-5

Index :

Aline Carvalho Rocha
Anice Holanda Nunes Maia
Cesario Rui Callou Filho
Maria Aparecida Ferreira Brandao
Nirla Gomes Guedes
Roberta Duarte Maia
Sheila Maria Santiago Borges
Wladia Teixeira de Morais

Insertion of the psychology student in the hospital: systematization and standard operating procedures for internships.

PRESENTATION

Since 1999, the psychology service at the Albert Sabin Children's Hospital (HIAS) has been a teaching-learning field for activities involving supervised clinical and hospital care. The largest number of trainees are students on compulsory professional internships in psychology, from public and private higher education institutions.

With the enactment of the new Internship Law in 2008, a new scenario emerged for organizing curricular internships. The Health Department of the State of Ceará (SESA) established new rules and a flowchart for the placement of interns and defined quotas for the distribution of vacancies in the state education network; it removed the autonomy of hospital managers to decide on the matter, extinguishing the local selection process. As a result, students began to be selected by Higher Education Institutions (HEIs), based on curricular criteria, as well as presenting themselves to the Service at different times, which posed a major challenge for homogeneous placement and the provision of a regular training process.

In view of the lack of homogeneity and continuity in the process of getting psychology students into the curricular internship field, there was a need to systematize the specific rules of this internship in line with those of the SESA. In view of the current situation, it is envisaged that Standard Operating Procedures (SOPs) will be drawn up to clarify the stages of the student's placement in the internship field, from the time they are requested by the Higher Education Institution (HEI) to the end of the curricular internship and the actions of the HIAS Psychology Department for the management of graduate internships.

Based on this project, the hospital in question will provide the HEIs with rules regarding the provision of vacancies; admission; monitoring; and the end of the internship in the teaching-learning process each semester. To this end, priority was given to defining the potential and weaknesses of HIAS as an internship field, as well as the construction and implementation of SOPs to guide the placement of psychology undergraduates. In this way, the project presented here will provide a perspective for discussing the organized and planned placement of students in the field of practice, contributing to a better quality training process.

Chapter 1

This Application Project, developed by Affinity Group C (GA C), is specifically immersed in the field of Health Education. The GA C meetings served as the basis for discussions of the problem situations, worked on systematically in the GROVE worksheet in which the problem was raised and then chosen (APPENDIX A).

The idea for the project arose from the lack of homogeneity and continuity in the process of introducing psychology students to the field of curricular internship in tertiary care. The aim is to standardize the internship practices of psychology students in a tertiary hospital in the city of Fortaleza, the Albert Sabin Children's Hospital (HIAS). Thus, a strategy is needed to develop Standard Operating Procedures (SOPs) that clarify the stages of the student's process in the internship field, from the time they are requested by the Higher Education Institution (HEI) to the end of the curricular internship.

Based on this project, the hospital in question will provide the HEIs with rules regarding the provision of vacancies, including the selection process; admission; monitoring; and the end of the internship in the teaching-learning sphere each semester. In addition, the definition of criteria will make the process fair, impartial and transparent.

Curricular internship, by its nature, is a compulsory activity established by the National Curricular Guidelines (DCN), in compliance with legal norms. It consists of staying at an organization that is willing to host the student for a pre-defined period, during which the trainee will carry out a set of activities considered relevant to the development of their professional experience and which also benefit the host organization. It is a time of learning in which the student, through guided work, comes into contact with the reality of the field of professional activity.

Specifically, the traineeship involves the trainee being integrated into the general activities of the granting entity, carrying out tasks in various functional areas, being integrated into a specific area or developing a unique activity of interest recognized by the host entity. In short, the role of the curricular internship is to encourage students to interact between "knowing" and "doing".

The application project presented here will be developed in a state-run tertiary pediatric hospital, HIAS. The hospital has approximately 330 beds and offers care in 22 medical specialties, including clinical and surgical emergencies, high-complexity procedures in oncology, neurosurgery, cardiac surgery and craniofacial surgery, as well as intensive care units and medium- and high-risk neonatal units. HIAS also has an interdisciplinary team made up of nurses, psychologists, physiotherapists, nutritionists, dentists, speech therapists, occupational therapists, social workers and pharmacists.

In addition to caring for children and adolescents, HIAS also carries out teaching and research activities, and in 2006 it was certified by the Ministries of Education and Health as a Teaching Hospital. In the institution's organizational process, the development of SOPs is an action backed by management and supported by the quality office. From this perspective, in the field of psychology, the academic internship began in 1999, without specific regulations from the Ceará State Health Department (SESA). Thus, the psychology department itself managed the internship together with the HIAS Study Center.

The academic internship began in 1999. At the time, internships were governed by Law No. 6.494 of December 7, 1977 (BRASIL, 1977) and there was no specific regulation by SESA/Ceará. Thus, the HIAS Study Center regulated the agreements with the HEIs.

To get the students on board, a course was offered every semester for psychology students and professionals, called *Psychological Assistance to Children with Cancer* (ANNEX A), on the basis of which interested students were selected to start the internship. Between 2000 and 2004, 10 courses and 10 selection processes were held, following the same methodology, with minor variations. Between 2004 and 2007, due to institutional problems, the course was suspended. Entry was now by selection with a written test and interview. Monitoring and supervision as described above prevailed.

The enactment of the new Internship Law (2008) created a new scenario for organizing internships. The Ceará State Health Department (SESA) established Ordinance No. 747/08, which made teaching and learning practices effective in the state network units, with the following determinations (CEARÁ, 2008).

The impact of the new internship rules in the Psychology Department, as shown in the empirical reference, has brought a major challenge for homogeneous integration and for offering a regular training process.

Faced with this scenario, attempts have been made to regularize the placement system, but it has undergone several changes and variations, described in detail later in the empirical reference. Some approaches have been tried, but they haven't taken hold, such as: an immersion reception outside of HIAS, with teachers and supervisors present, and meetings during the semester to monitor training.

In addition, there are actions that are considered necessary and important, but are not carried out: individual assessment, whether summative or formative; an identification and monitoring form for each trainee; collection of the written intervention plan and the internship report at the end of the semester is optional; Procedures and guidelines for psychology activities by hospital sector (APPENDIX B).

In view of the above, it is understood that HIAS, as a teaching hospital, as well as providing care and research, has in its essence/mission a formative character in health, which is concerned with the curricular formation of psychology undergraduates. Bernardes (2012) emphasizes the pace of dialogue and debate about the training of these students, despite the fact that many courses are at a high pace of execution, finishing the implementation or evaluating their curricula, as determined by the new DCN, approved by the Ministry of Education in 2004 (BRASIL, 2004).

Recognizing its physical, human resource and organizational structural limits and the need for quality care, HIAS sets a limit on the number of student interns at the hospital, with quotas set by SESA. In this way, the project presented here will provide a perspective for discussing the organized and planned insertion of students in the field of practice, contributing to a better quality training process.

To this end, priority was given to defining the potential and weaknesses of HIAS as an internship field, as well as the construction and implementation of SOPs to guide the inclusion of psychology undergraduates in it.

The idea for the application project was consolidated by identifying aspects that underpinned its relevance, namely: incompatibility between supply and demand; no forecast of the number of students per semester; quotas are set by the SESA, which is not immersed in the day-to-day educational approach of the hospital; the department responsible for analyzing requests from HEIs does not have a single period set aside for analyzing the feasibility of the internship and the selection process; there are no criteria for evaluating requests from the HEIs; the psychology department is unaware of the HEIs' contribution to the service; there is no protocol for guiding, monitoring, developing and concluding the internship. This scenario has repercussions throughout the internship process, from the analysis of requests to the development of the internship itself.

In view of the above, it is understood that the situational diagnosis presented of the internship in psychology implies a deficiency in the systematization of the process of inserting psychology students into the graduate internship. Thus, the application project proposal is important for the entire organizational and educational process of the service.

Chapter 2

2.1 General Objective

- Systematizing the process of placement of graduate psychology students in a tertiary hospital.

2.2 Specific objectives

- Evaluate the current systematized process, defining its strengths and weaknesses;

- To build and implement Standard Operating Procedures for the placement of undergraduate psychology students in a tertiary hospital.

Chapter 3

3 REFERENCES

.1 Theoretical framework

Historically, the recognition of psychology as a health profession in Brazil is recent. The profession has been regulated for 51 years and has built up many of its theoretical references based on an approach and, consequently, an education focused on individual clinical practice. Its insertion in public health is still timid when compared to other professions.

In 1986, the 8ª National Health Conference was held, the main moment in the history of the Brazilian Health Reform. It was a landmark of intense political work, in which some important sectoral political leadership positions provided political articulation between parties, union organizers and the population.

The Brazilian Health Reform gave rise to the SUS in the 1988 Constitution. However, it was only with the drafting and approval of the infra-constitutional legislation known as the "Organic Health Laws" (Laws No. 8.080 and 8.142) that the general guidelines and organization of the system were determined (CARVALHO, 2001).

Based on the Organic Health Laws, the SUS had its guiding principles established, such as universality, which understands health as a right of all and a duty of the Public Power to offer services and actions that guarantee health care. The principle of comprehensiveness states that the individual needs of the subject should always guide health care, even if this is not the need of the majority of the population, including health care from promotion to rehabilitation, with a focus on the individual or the collective. The principle of equity means that, even with the social disparity that exists in Brazil, there is a need to have equal opportunities to use the Unified Health System (SUS) (BRASIL, 2000).

Based on these movements of the Health Reform, Psychology as a profession is evident in the process of interlocution with public policies for the training of health professionals and, above all, with the DCN, which are the fruit of the Health Reform Movement, and also with the conceptions of health-disease that reflect the interest in a transformation in the training of health professionals.

The DCN came about by proposing a reform in the training of health professionals, with the Medicine and Nursing courses first being covered in 2001 and, later, the other health courses. Thus, based on the DCN for Health, the National Education Council (CNE), through the Chamber of Higher Education, instituted the DCN for undergraduate courses in Psychology, with Resolution No. 8 of May 7, 2004, which establishes competencies conceptualized as knowledge, skills and attitudes that enable interaction and multiprofessional action for the benefit of individuals and communities, promoting health for all. The competences established in the Opinion of the Ministry of Education and Culture (MEC) point to: health care, decision-making, communication, administration and management and permanent education (BRASIL, 2004).

Article 3 of the DCN for undergraduate courses in Psychology states that the central goal of the undergraduate course in Psychology is to train psychologists for professional practice, research and teaching

8

in psychology, and that it must ensure a degree based on a number of principles and commitments. These include item IV - critical understanding of the country's social, economic, cultural and political phenomena, which is fundamental to the exercise of citizenship and the profession - and item V - acting in different contexts, considering social needs and human rights, with a view to promoting the quality of life of individuals, groups, organizations and communities (BRASIL, 2004).

These principles can only be acquired fully and effectively when the student is inserted into a practice scenario. Article 17 of the DCN states that academic activities must provide elements for the acquisition of the basic competences, skills and knowledge necessary for professional practice (BRASIL, 2004). Thus, these activities should, in a systematic and gradual way, bring the trainee closer to the professional practice corresponding to the competences envisaged for the graduate.

When thinking about teacher training in psychology, the same guidelines establish the minimum necessary criteria, among them the workload for Psychology Teacher Training, which should be at least 800 (eight hundred) hours, plus the workload of the Psychology course, encompassing: a) Content specific to the area of Education: 500 (five hundred) hours; b) Supervised Curricular Internship: 300 (three hundred) hours (BRASIL, 2004).

The activities related to Teacher Training, to be assimilated and acquired by complementing the Psychology course, will be offered to all undergraduate students, who may or may not choose to take them. Students who satisfactorily fulfill all the requirements of the complementary project will have their degree in Psychology certified on their diplomas.

Within the specific scope of the internship in the undergraduate course, art. 19 states that academic planning must ensure, in terms of workload and study plans, the student's involvement in individual and team activities, which include, among other integrative practices aimed at developing skills and competencies in situations of varying complexity, representative of effective professional practice, in the form of a supervised internship (BRASIL, 2004).

Thus, supervised internships are a set of training activities, programmed and directly supervised by members of the teaching staff of the training institution, and seek to ensure the consolidation and articulation of the competences established. They aim to ensure that the trainee comes into contact with situations, contexts and institutions, enabling knowledge, skills and attitudes to be put into practice in professional actions, and it is recommended that supervised internship activities be spread throughout the course.

The basic supervised internship will include the development of practices that integrate the competences and skills provided for in the common core. Paragraph 2 of the DCN also states that each specific supervised internship will include the development of practices that integrate the competencies, skills and knowledge that define each emphasis proposed by the course project. In line with this, Art. 23 states that the supervised internship activities must be documented in such a way as to enable the development of the competences and skills envisaged to be assessed according to the institution's standards (BRASIL, 2004).

Art. 24 also states that the institution may recognize activities carried out by students in other institutions, as long as they contribute to the development of the skills and competences provided for in the course project. In addition, §3 states that basic and specific internships must make up at least 15% (fifteen percent) of the total course workload (BRASIL, 2004).

According to the Law of Guidelines and Bases of National Education - LDBEM, the scenario of Higher Education is defined among other purposes as a sword to stimulate knowledge of current problems focusing on the provision of specialized service to the population. The Curricular Guidelines welcome the importance of meeting social demands, highlighting the SUS, inviting training institutions to change their pedagogical practices in an attempt to bring social reality to the teaching staff and students, working towards a horizontal and interventional action.

The qualified presence of psychology in the SUS was the theme adopted by the Brazilian Association of Psychology Teaching (ABEP) for the implementation of initiatives aimed at including public health in psychology training courses in Brazil. In 2006, with funding from the Pan American Health Organization (PAHO) and in partnership with the Federal Council of Psychology (CFP), 37 regional workshops and one national workshop were held, which resulted in systematized proposals for defining the new curricular pedagogical plans for psychology courses (SPINK, 2007).

According to Paulo Freire, the teaching-learning process presupposes respect for the student's cultural background, as well as their knowledge built up in community practice. Active methodologies are based on a significant theoretical principle: autonomy. Therefore, contemporary education must presuppose the student's ability to self-manage or self-govern their learning process. Teaching requires the autonomy and dignity of each individual; it is the foundation for an education that takes into account the individual as a being who constructs their own history (FREIRE, 1983).

Indeed, it is through the teaching-learning process that we can generate knowledge. University extension makes knowledge a tool in the pedagogical process, contributing both to the training of the learner and to the integration of the teaching-service-community process. In this process, the supervised internship, a fundamental moment in the apprentice's training, consists of theory and practice, constantly seeking out reality in order to develop work in the training of educators. From this perspective, the supervised internship should lead the trainee to various practices and various ways of being a professional. Since internships follow a traditional cycle, which consists of observation, supervision and participation, all of which are monitored and supervised by the teacher responsible for the teaching practice/supervised internship (MARCHIORI; MELO; MELO, 2011).

According to the Internship Law No. 11.788, of September 25, 2008, art.1: "The internship is a supervised school educational act, developed in the work environment, which aims to prepare students who are attending regular education in higher education institutions for productive work [...]. § 2 The internship is aimed at learning the skills required for professional activity and at contextualizing the curriculum, with the aim of developing the student for life as a citizen and for work" (BRASIL, 2008).

It is important to note that the Code of Professional Ethics for Psychologists highlights the training process in Art. 17 - "It is the responsibility of teaching psychologists or supervisors to clarify, inform, guide and demand that students observe the principles and norms contained in this code" (CFP, 2005).

As well as the code of ethics, the Federal Council of Psychology (CFP) refers to educational practices related to internships, reaffirming the importance of commitment in the professional formation of psychology, in resolutions that encourage responsible work, the valuing of authorship by the intern and the observance of technical and ethical aspects. Here are some aspects of the law involving education, according to CFP resolution 001/2009: Art. 3.

> In the case of psychological services provided at schools and internship camps, the record must include the identification and signature of the person responsible for the service, as well as that of the intern; Sole paragraph. The technical supervisor must ask the trainee to record all activities and events that occur with the users of the psychological service provided (CFP, 2009).

Finally, it is believed that learning is necessarily a way of practicing knowledge, of appropriating its specific processes. What is fundamental about knowledge is not its status as a product, but its process. In fact, knowledge is the result of a historical and collective construction. For Paulo Freire,

> "...reading the world precedes reading the word and reading the word implies continuing to read the world. ...this movement from the world to the word and from the word to the world is always present. A movement in which the spoken word flows from the world even through the reading we do of it." (FREIRE, 1982, p. 22).

[2] .2 Contextual Reference: Albert Sabin Children's Hospital and the Psychology Service

HIAS is an organ of the state public administration - Executive Branch, subordinate to the Health Secretariat of the State of Ceará, located at Rua Tertuliano Sales, n°. 544, in the Vila União neighborhood in Fortaleza-Ceará, in a physical structure composed of a central building and annexes, such as the Pediatric Cancer Center, the Cancer Reference and Diagnostic Center, the Human Milk Bank and the teaching support structure area.

The building includes ombudsman, outpatient rooms, dentistry, psychology, speech therapy, social work, physiotherapy, SESMT, Research Ethics Committee; Hospital Pharmacy; Material and Sterilization Center; Surgical Center, Laboratory Services (routine and specialized diagnostic and complementary tests), Imaging Sector (Electrocardiogram, Electroencephalogram, Tomography, X-Ray, Digestive Endoscopy, Bronchoscopy, Trancranial Doppler), cafeterias, Immunology Reference Center, Quality Office, Waste Management, CCIH, Children's City and administrative area: SAME, Cost, Assets, Medical Accounts, Human Development Service, General Management, Clinical, Technical, Financial Administrative.

According to information in the printed institutional agenda for 2013[1], the hospital was inaugurated on December 26, 1952 as the Fortaleza Children's Hospital with the aim of housing sick children, mainly from the interior of the state, in three wards. Its initiative was considered pioneering, as until then there had been no institution in Ceará exclusively dedicated to childcare. In 1976, its new headquarters were inaugurated, where it still stands today. On July 17, 1977, on the occasion of Dr. Sabin's visit to the hospital, the state government decreed that it be renamed the Albert Sabin Children's Hospital.

At the beginning of its activities, the hospital only offered General Pediatrics, Maternal and Child Care and Neurology services. Today, with a tertiary level of care in pediatrics, its activities include clinical and surgical emergencies,

---

[3] Every year, the Albert Sabin Children's Hospital (HIAS) distributes a printed institutional agenda containing its history. The information that begins this paragraph contains data taken from this agenda.

high-complexity procedures in Oncology, Neurosurgery, Cardiac Surgery and Craniofacial Surgery, as well as Intensive Care Units and medium and high-risk Neonatal Units. With a specialty in 22 medical specialties and fourteen technical diagnostic and therapy services, HIAS has approximately 330 beds, including 122 clinical, 69 surgical, 42 intensive care, 22 day hospital, 60 home care, 8 chronic, among others.

In order to carry out its activities, HIAS has the technology and equipment to make its final and support processes faster and safer. The clinic's main products are: inpatient care, outpatient care, home care and support services.

In terms of teaching and research, it promotes medical residency, internships in medicine and nursing, curricular internships in nursing, physiotherapy, psychology, social work, dentistry and pharmacy, organizes technical and scientific events, and is also a field of research for various projects approved by its own ethics committee.

The strategic planning defined the mission as: "To provide tertiary care to children and adolescents, in a safe and humanized way, as a teaching and research institution", with the future vision of being international pediatric excellence in quaternary care, teaching and research, with socio-environmental responsibility, establishing ethics, humanization, commitment, participation, professional appreciation, efficiency and credibility as values.

In 2006, it was certified by the Ministries of Education and Health as a Teaching Hospital, through Interministerial Ordinance No. 337, of February 14, and contracted on December 12 of the same year by Ordinance No. 3145, thus expanding its competencies. Recognized as a National Reference Center for the Promotion of Child and Adolescent Health, HIAS values the quality and continuous improvement of its services offered to patients from all over Ceará and neighboring states.

In the area of teaching, research and extension, HIAS is coordinated by the Center for Studies and Research and involves Schooling, Graduation and Post-Graduation projects, as well as activities in extension, continuing education and research (ANNEX C). HIAS's activities in these three areas will be described in more detail below, according to a survey carried out by Borges (2006) and HIAS (2012).

The schooling project called Novo Futuro (New Future) was created in 2000 in partnership with the Futura channel and with the support of the state departments of Education and Administration. It offers employees the opportunity to complete their studies on HIAS premises and within their working hours. Currently, 82 employees have completed elementary school, 121 have completed secondary school, six have entered higher education and six have already completed a higher education course.

The graduate area includes the medical and nursing internships, curricular internships (medicine, nursing, physiotherapy, social work, dentistry, hospital pharmacy, bromatology and psychology - all in the pediatric area) and the HIAS scholarship program.

The lato sensu postgraduate program has been in existence for 36 years, and by 2012 had trained 463 residents in the areas of general pediatrics, pediatric surgery, pediatric cancerology, orthopedics and traumatology, hematology-hemotherapy, onco-hematology, gastroenterology, cardiology, nephrology, intensive care medicine, neonatology and pulmonology. In addition to the medical residency program, HIAS is a training ground for the multi-professional residency program of the Walter Cantídio University Hospital and the Ceará State Health Department.

The extension area is responsible for supervising projects that meet the demands of the hospital's staff, technical staff, users and the community. The following projects have been developed: Fearless Surgery, ABC Mais Saúde, Children's City, New Future, Sound Therapy, Toy Library, Love, Spelling HIAS, Mão Amiga, Choir.

Permanent Education has a Permanent Education Committee and develops activities in the Visiting Professor project, the Telemedicine University Network and Specialized Courses in partnership with the State University of Ceará.

In the field of research, HIAS has a Research and Development Center, which is made up of a multidisciplinary board and its own Research Ethics Committee. The center works through workshops on project development, database analysis management and the writing of scientific articles. The lines of research currently being carried out at HIAS are: Nutrition and metabolism in children and adolescents; Neonatology; Infectious and parasitic diseases; Pediatric nephrology; Oncology, hematology and hemotherapy; Acute and chronic pneumonia in children; Pediatric surgery; Rheumatological and other autoimmune diseases in pediatrics; Genetic diseases in children and adolescents; Respiratory and motor physiotherapy; Endocrine diseases in pediatrics; Occupational therapy in pediatrics.

In the teaching context, the psychology department is not formally part of the organizational structure, but it does work effectively with the institution. The small number of professionals limits the psychology department, which is organized and linked to specific clinics and assists other HIAS wards.[2]

Psychology's main area of focus at the hospital is in the Onco-Hematology Service, which is currently encompassed by the Pediatric Cancer Center (CPC). The determination of Ministerial Order GM/MS No. 3535/1998, replaced by GM/MS Order No. 741/2005, that high-complexity oncology units should adhere to the National Humanization Policy and provide multidisciplinary support, with technical-assistance activities carried out on an outpatient and inpatient basis, on a routine and emergency basis, in various areas, including clinical psychology (BRASIL, 2005) led to the implementation of the Psychology Unit in the Oncology Department in 1998.

The other areas covered are the Adolescent Health Program (PROSAD), which was the pioneering area of inclusion and is currently being restructured. The inpatient units that don't have an exclusive psychology team are served by a system of requests for assessment and/or psychological care, which are only intended for the most critical cases due to the high demand from the institution. This offer is far below the existing repressed demand and is the target of actions to supply psychology professionals.

The Comprehensive Cleft Care Center (NAIF) and the Orientation and Stimulation Center for Infants (NOEL) are staffed by psychologists, as is the specialty outpatient clinic.

Institutional and formalized partnerships are established with pathology associations in order to expand patient care. Psychology's work is characterized in the table below:

---

[2] Every year, the Albert Sabin Children's Hospital (HIAS) distributes a printed institutional agenda containing its history.

The information from note 1 to this paragraph contains data taken from this agenda.

Chart 1 - HIAS work units, according to direct action, number of professionals, action through partnerships. Fortaleza, 2013

	Direct action	No. of professionals	Acting through partnerships	No. of professionals
Operating Units	Prog rammed Adolescents/Nurses HIAS.	01	-	-
	Pediatric Cancer Center (CPC).	02	Peter's Association Pan, through social programs.	01
	Guidance and Infant Stimulation (NOEL) and Integrated Cleft Care Center (NAIF):	02, one of whom is exclusively a preceptor.	-	-
	In the Special Patients Unit (UPE),	-	Brazilian Association of Amyotrophy Spinal.	01
	Rheumatology Department	-	Support Group for Rheumatic Patients in Ceará	01
TOTAL				08

Psychology's work in the hospital context is recognized through the specialty of Hospital Psychology, according to CFP Resolution No. 013/2007, which defines the attributions for this field of work:

> Works in health care institutions, participating in the provision of secondary or tertiary level health care services [...] Cares for patients, family members and/or those responsible for the patient; members of the community within their area of activity; members of the multi-professional team and possibly administrative staff, with a view to the physical and emotional well-being of the patient. It offers and develops activities at different levels of treatment, with its main task being the assessment and monitoring of psychological intercurrences in patients who are or will be undergoing medical procedures, basically with a view to promoting and/or recovering physical and mental health. It promotes interventions aimed at the doctor/patient, patient/family, and patient/patient and patient relationships in relation to the process of becoming ill, hospitalization and the emotional repercussions that emerge from this process. The support can be directed at patients undergoing clinical or surgical care, in the different medical specialties. Different types of intervention can be developed, depending on demand and the training of the specific professional; among these are: psychotherapeutic care; psychotherapeutic groups; psychoprophylaxis groups; outpatient and Intensive Care Unit care; emergency care; wards in general; psychomotricity in the hospital context; diagnostic assessment; psychodiagnosis; consultancy and interconsultancy. When working with a multidisciplinary team, preferably an interdisciplinary one, they take part in decisions regarding the conduct to be adopted by the team, with the aim of promoting support and security for the patient and family, providing information pertinent to their area of activity, as well as in the form of a reflection group, in which support and management are geared towards possible operational and/or subjective difficulties of the team members (CFP, 2007, p.p.21-22).

Psychology's work in the teaching/learning area is supported by legal frameworks, such as Law No. 4119/1962 of 1962, which states that "students' internships and practical observations may be carried out in other local institutions, at the discretion of the course professors" (BRASIL, 1962, p. 3). This is how the extramural internship modality is sustained, with hospitals being successive fields of insertion over the years.

In addition, the practice with undergraduate students in the hospital context is guided by CFP Resolution No. 003/2007, which sets out responsibilities for the preceptor psychologist:

> ...Without prejudice to the private nature of the professional activity, the psychologist may delegate duties to trainees as a form of training [...] The supervising psychologist must be registered with the Regional Council of the jurisdiction in which he or she carries out his or her activity [...].The granting of internships will only occur in cases where the didactic nature of the activity to be carried out by the intern is characterized and under conditions in which it is possible to supervise the work [...] The psychologist responsible is obliged to personally verify the technical training of their intern, supervising them and being directly responsible for the proper application of psychological methods and techniques and respect for professional ethics (CFP, 2007, p. 19).

CFP Resolution No. 013/2007 defines that hospital psychologists also work in higher education institutions and/or study and research centers, with the aim of improving or specializing professionals in their area of competence, or complementing the training of other health professionals at secondary or higher level, including *lato* and *stricto sensu* postgraduate courses (CFP, 2007).

The practice of psychology at HIAS also follows the consensus and guidelines of the scientific societies in the field, including the Brazilian Society of Hospital Psychology (SBPH); the Brazilian Society of Psycho-Oncology (SBPO); the Psychology Department of the Brazilian Association of Intensive Care Medicine (AMIB); and the Brazilian Association of Collective Health (ABRASCO), among others. Through the affiliation of professionals and/or participation in scientific events, with the presentation of papers, there is an updating and improvement of the references for action, which include psychological assessment; brief focal psychotherapies; operative groups; psychoprophylaxis; humanization; welcoming and palliative care.

Of the above-mentioned units, the CPC and NOEL/NAIF are the areas of the Psychology Service in which psychology graduate internships are offered, with the CPC being the area with the most placements.

3.3 Empirical reference: experience/history of the oncology service at HIAS in the area of teaching

The Psychology Service at HIAS is a teaching-learning field for basic internships, technical visits, observation of practices, intermediate internships and professional internships at the end of the course, involving supervised clinical and hospital care. It is made up of five professionals from the institution itself, three of whom act as preceptors.

The main students involved are undergraduates enrolled in compulsory internships in psychology courses at public and private higher education institutions, which have been offered since 1999.

That year, the academic internship at HIAS began with two UFC interns in the Onco-Hematology Service. The field of psychology soon proved to be very attractive to students and higher education institutions, and the Onco-Hematology Service began to receive around four to six students per semester.

At the time, internships were governed by Law No. 6.494 of December 7, 1977 (BRASIL, 1977) and there was no specific regulation by SESA/Ceará. Thus, the HIAS Study Centre regulated agreements with the Federal University of Ceará (UFC) and the University of Fortaleza (UNIFOR), the two higher education institutions offering psychology courses in Ceará, but there was a reasonable balance between demand and supply of places, and the relationship between the Psychology Service and the higher education institutions took place in order to organize an internship programme in Hospital Psychology.

To get the students on board, a course was offered every semester for psychology students and professionals, called *Psychological Assistance to Children with Cancer, with a* workload of between 20 and 24 hours, taught by professionals from the oncopediatrics team and by guest professors.

On the last day of the course, a selection was made of the number of students interested in the internship corresponding to the vacancies defined by the Psychology Department. The selection was made using the *role-playing* technique, with a dramatization of a bedside care situation for a child and his mother, and a written test and group interview.

Between 2000 and 2004, 10 courses and 10 selection processes were held, following the same methodology, with minor variations. Rules for the internship time limit were not properly established.

After being selected, the students began their practicums in the same week. The first part of the internship included a process of observing the practice, in which the students accompanied the service psychologist in her routine. There was weekly supervision of the internship, lasting 2 hours, in which the cases were discussed, making an exercise of correlation with the techniques and theories of psychology.

Between 2004 and 2007, due to institutional problems, the course was suspended. Entry was then by selection, with a written test and interview. Those approved started in a regular week and there was introductory training through one-off classes. Monitoring and supervision as described above prevailed.

The enactment of the new Internship Law (2008) gave rise to a new scenario for organizing internships. The Ceará State Health Department (SESA) established Ordinance No. 747/08, which made teaching and learning practices effective in the state network units, with the following determinations (CEARÁ, 2008):

1) Based on the state-education network agreement process, the distribution of places in the state network must comply with the quotas of 50% for state education institutions, 35% for federal institutions and 15% for private institutions.

2) Institutions of higher education or technical education began to submit their needs at the beginning of each semester;

3) At SESA, the demands were analyzed in terms of the formal aspects of the agreements and the installed capacity defined by the health units, and were then sent to the requested SESA Network units for final appraisal.

4) After analysis by the Network's health unit, the answers became sent to SESA to inform the educational institution.

5) It was only after the educational institution had received a response from SESA that contact could be made between the educational institution and the SESA network health unit, including to

establish a partnership with the
responsible for monitoring the teaching practices requested.

The impact of the new internship rules on the Psychology Department was as follows: the selection process was abolished; students were now received
selected by the HEIs according to curricular criteria; they began to deal with different deadlines for the arrival and integration of students, which posed a major challenge for homogeneous integration and the provision of a regular training process.

From 2010 onwards, extension students were included and the Psychology Department became a field of practice for multiprofessional health residencies. The regular areas of teaching practice are Oncology, the care centers for patients with cleft lip and palate and those with early childhood pediatric syndromes. Occasionally, internships have been offered in the Cardiology and Nephrology departments.

Since 1999, 138 students have completed internships at the Psychology Department:

Graph 1 - Distribution of interns in the HIAS Psychology Department between 1999 and 2013, Fortaleza, CE, 2013.

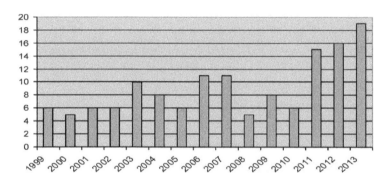

Until 2013, the students came from the Federal University of Ceará (UFC), the University of Fortaleza (UNIFOR), the Intensive Technology College (FATECI) and Faculdades do Nordeste (FANOR).

With regard to the process of training students for teaching-learning practices in psychology in the hospital field, currently 13 courses have been held with syllabus content on psychological care for hospitalized children and adolescents. As a strategy for socializing internship experiences, three academic meetings were held between the 2011.2 and 2012.2 semesters.

Faced with this scenario, attempts have been made to regularize the student insertion system, and there have been several changes and variations in its methodology, resulting in an inhomogeneous program with discontinued actions in many cases. Currently, the system works on the basis of the following methodological strategy:

1) About three months before the start of each semester, the Psychology Department defines the number

of vacancies for each subordinate unit, which is decided at a meeting between the precepting psychologists;

2) The number of vacancies is based on the renewal of internships, which are guaranteed to students from previous semesters who wish to continue in the field;

3) The number of places is informed to the Study Center, which sends it to SESA, according to the quotas for each type of HEI: In the case of Psychology, 50% for the Federal University of Ceará (UECE), 35% for the Federal University of Ceará (UFC) and 15% for private institutions;

4) The HEIs send their demands to the SESA via the Single Protocol System no later than 60 days before the start of the semester;

5) After receiving the demand, the Psychology Service preceptors actively seek out the supervising teachers to identify the contacts of the candidates for the internship;

6) They are then given a form (ANNEX D) with their academic profile so that the preceptors can propose intervention projects that are consistent with this profile;

7) At the beginning of the semester, students are welcomed individually or by HEI, and within a period of approximately two weeks, they agree on their days and times of practice, in accordance with the legal requirements and the organizational rationale of the internship. This stage also includes an introduction to the service, guided tours and institutional observation under an immersion regime, paying attention to the environment, professionals, users, routines, emergency situations, relationships, visual and interpersonal communication, among other aspects. A script of activities (ANNEX B) is provided for knowledge and analysis, basic bibliography is indicated and ideas are exchanged about the intervention project;

8) Once this stage has been completed, the first part of the theoretical-methodological orientation process takes place. This consists of a round table discussion about the students' academic career, their studies and directions, as well as their expectations and their way of perceiving the hospital. In sub-groups, they analyze the activity guide and then report their impressions and questions, which are then discussed with the preceptors for a new synthesis of understanding. Ethical standards are also discussed;

9) Interventions begin to be carried out through a gradual process of insertion after the period of observation, and technical supervision takes place every Friday. However, the preceptorship process is continuous, taking place before or after the interventions during the academic practice periods in which a psychologist is available to provide the necessary guidance;

10) About a month later, a 24-hour course is offered on *Psychological Assistance for Hospitalized Children and Adolescents* (ANNEX A), so that the student goes to this theoretical moment more in tune with reality and with their doubts better identified;

11) At the end of each semester, an academic meeting is held to conclude the term, in which the students produce reports on their experiences in the form of scientific papers and present them to the professionals in the services, fields of practice and teaching supervisors. At this event, there is also a retrospective of experiences and a tribute to the graduates. It is a time for closing cycles and saying

goodbye, where the emotional bonds developed are reaffirmed.

In general, the aforementioned process responds to current challenges, but there are some "critical nodes" that contribute to a lack of homogeneity and consolidation of the methodological steps used.

With regard to item 3, the establishment of quotas means that there are often vacancies in the categories of public HEIs, which in general the Psychology Department has the autonomy to redistribute to private HEIs, but this is only possible through a considerable effort to actively seek out supervising teachers in time to obtain clear and definitive information and within a timeframe that makes it possible for students to be placed. Some HEIs manage to respond because their pre-registration rules allow for the prior identification of students, others do not, because there is no pre-registration and it is only after definitive registration that there is effective delineation, but it is late compared to the SESA flow. The latter use the strategy of over-estimating the need for places at SESA in order to guarantee the timing of the request. However, as this is only a projection, it is only through telephone contact with the teachers that it is possible to work out a real and fair distribution.

With regard to item 4, the problems relate to the arrival of internship application files at HIAS and the coordination of Psychology preceptors within varying timeframes. Regarding item 11, there is little presence of teaching supervisors.

Finally, they point to methodological strategies that were applied on a one-off basis, such as evaluation meetings between field preceptors and supervising teachers during the semester and an integrated meeting between students, preceptors and supervising teachers at the beginning of the semester, outside the hospital environment.

In the category of not applied and perceived as necessary and relevant, there is a set of actions such as: *feedback* to students and supervising teachers during the course of teaching-learning practices; standardized assessment instruments; individual *feedback* to students at the end of the internship; the requirement to submit reports and the organization of the scientific production process resulting from the internship.

Chapter 4
4 INTERVENTION PROPOSAL

4.1 Current and desired situation

4.1.1 Current situation

      The intervention proposal will identify the current situation in order to explain the problems encountered, serving as a basis for defining goals that respond to the proposed objectives. The current situation of the undergraduate psychology internship at HIAS is as follows:

1. Failure by the Psychology Service to offer a regular number of vacancies in line with the quotas established by SESA;

2. Failure to publicize the offer of the Psychology Service to HEIs and to survey the real demand forecast by them;

3. Irresolution of a single period for simultaneous analysis by the Psychology Service of all internship applications from HEIs;

4. The lack of standardized criteria for evaluating HEI applications and selecting students in the face of demand outstripping supply and the lack of knowledge of HEI counterparts to HIAS;

5. Imprecision in the process of welcoming trainees, as well as in the monitoring and evaluation of traineeship practices during the course of the traineeship;

6. Deficiency in the process of building competencies, skills and attitudes for internship practices and strategies for completing them.

4.1.2 Desired situation

      In view of the current situation, and considering the possibility of the granting institution playing a leading role in the process of undergraduate internships in the hospital field, it is envisaged that a SOP and guidelines will be drawn up by the HIAS Psychology Service for the management of undergraduate internships, in line with the rules determined by SESA and HIAS, so as to cover the axes of provision, admission, monitoring and closure.

      In terms of provision, the following desired actions are envisaged:

1. Define the supply of psychology services on a regular basis;

2. Publicize the psychology service on offer at the HEIs and, in the light of this, carry out a survey of the real demand expected by the HEIs;

3. Establish a single period of simultaneous analysis by the Psychology Department of all internship request processes from HEIs;

4. Determine standardized criteria for evaluating HEI applications and selecting students in cases where

demand exceeds supply;

On the <u>admissions front</u>, the following actions are outlined:

1. Organize the process for welcoming trainees and agreeing on the intervention project based on the curricular demands of the HEIs;

2. Outline the process of building competencies, skills and attitudes for the start of internship practices;

The following actions are placed on the <u>monitoring axis:</u>

1. To detail the process of monitoring and evaluating internship practices in psychology during their course, including assistance and encouragement for scientific production;

Finally, in the <u>closing section of the internship, the</u> aim is to:

2. Set up strategies for concluding internship experiences through the presentation of scientific papers and socialization processes, in partnership with higher education institutions;

3. Determine the process for evaluating and documenting completed psychology graduate internship practices.

4.2 Baselines

The baseline provides the reference points to be used for comparing the current situation, the situation to be modified and the desired situation, indicating the actual progress of the intervention project. It therefore includes the best estimates for the approach and for problem solving, as successful points after completed tasks.

In this application project, a baseline is presented that explains the starting point and the indicators for evaluating effectiveness.

Table 2 - Description of the current situation and results indicators, according to application project proposal. Fortaleza, 2013

Current situation	Result indicator(s)
The Psychology Service is not offering enough places on a regular basis;	Resolution delimiting the number of places offered by the Service in each academic semester;
Failure to publicize the psychology services on offer at the HEIs and to survey actual and expected demand by them;	Correspondence received by theIES with the announcement of the vacancies on offer;
	Correspondence received from HEIs with demand projections for the following semester;

Irresolution of a single period for simultaneous analysis by the Psychology of all internship application processes from HEIs;	Resolution defining a six-month period with deadlines for the analysis of cases;
The lack of standardized criteria for evaluating HEI applications and selecting students in the face of the demand-versus-supply scenario. lack of knowledge of the HEIs' counterparts to HIAS;	The service's standard operating procedure (SOP) with analysis and selection criteria;
Imprecision of the reception process for trainees , as well as the monitoring and evaluation of internship practices during the course of the internship;	Standard operating procedures (SOPs) containing the stages of reception and the monitoring and evaluation of internship practices;
Deficiency in the process of building competencies, skills and attitudes for internship practices and strategies for completing them.	Standard operating procedures (SOP) that contain the benchmarks for carrying out the activities and for completing the internship practices, containing evaluation and documentation aspects.

4.3 Intervention actions

The implementation of this project includes the actions listed below, which will be presented to the Psychology Service team for discussion, appropriation, improvement and development.

With a view to the effectiveness of this project, the actions are arranged in chronological order, in relation to the execution deadline and in hierarchical order, according to the weight of the importance that the action has for achieving the objective, defined as a percentage.

Considering the end of the 2013.1 academic semester, the actions are planned to be developed for the 2013.2 semester and implemented in the Service for the 2014.1 semester.

Table 3 - Description of the actions suggested in the application project, in order chronological and hierarchical. Fortaleza, 2013

ACTION	SCHEDULE	HIERARCHY % WEIGHT
Drawing up a standard operating procedure (SOP) for the Service containing criteria for selecting trainees, taking into account the quotas pre-established by the SESA, the counterpart and the performance of the HEIs in previous semesters.	1	15
Drawing up a standard operating procedure (SOP) containing: a) the reception stages; b) monitoring and c) evaluation of internship practices.	2	25

Drawing up standard operating procedures (SOPs) containing: a) the benchmarks for carrying out practical activities and b) for completing internship practices, containing evaluation and documentation aspects.	3	25
Issuing a resolution that delimits the number of places offered by the Service in each academic semester, taking into account the quotas pre-established by the SESA.	4	15
Exchanges of letters with the HEIs about vacancies offered and requests for projected vacancies.	5	05
Establishment of a standard operating procedure (SOP) with an annual flowchart defining the precise period for analyzing the processes each semester.	6	15

4.4 Resources

Table 4 - Description of the actions suggested in the application project, according to responsible, beginning and end, resources and results indicators. Fortaleza, 2013

Action	Responsible	Home	End	Resources	)Result indicators
Preparation of the service 's standard operating procedure (SOP) with selection criteriaof trainees, who take into account the quotas pre-established by SESA , the counterparty performance IES in previous semesters.	Psychology internship coordinator at HIAS	Aug/13	Aug/13	Computer Leaves paperwork A4	Servipo SOP with analysis criteria selection, duly prepared and approved by the circumstances responsible for HIAS.
Elaboration of standard operating procedure (SOP) containing: a) the steps of the (b) monitoring and (c) evaluating internship practices.	Psychology internship coordinator at HIAS	Aug/13	Aug/13	Printer cartridges Legislation normative documents	POP properly prepared, and approved by the responsible for HIAS.

Elaboration of standard operating procedures (SOP) containing: a) the references for the realization activities practicesb)for conclusion of internship practices, containing evaluation documents.	Psychology internship coordinator at HIAS	Aug/13	Aug/13	related. Ballpoint pen. Pen drive.	POP properly prepared, and approved by the responsible for HIAS.
Edition of a resolution delimit the number of places offered by the Service in each semester, taking into account the quotas pre-established by the SESA.	Psychology internship coordinator at HIAS.	Oct/13	Oct/13	Resources humans: Coordinator, preceptors and trainees. ADINS	Updated resolution.
Tro cade correspondence with HEIs about vacancies offered and requests for projected vacancies.	Psychology internship coordinator at HIAS.	Nov/13	Nov/13	Coordinator Coordinator of the Study Center.	Correspondence received by theIES applicants, at the end of the previous academic semester, with the announcement of the vacancies offered. Correspondence received from HEIs with demand projection for the following semester.
Establishing a procedure standard operating procedure (SOP) with annual flowchart with defined precise period for analysis processes each semester.	Internshi p coordinator in Psychology at HIAS	Nov/13	Nov/13		POPcom establishment of half-yearly periods updated with precise deadlines for analyzing processes.
Appr oval of standard operating procedures (SOP)	Coordinator of the Study Center	Aug/13	Nov/13		POP validated by Study Center

Vali dity standard operating procedures (SOP)	ADINS Coordinator	Aug/13	Nov/13			POP validated by Advisory Development Institutional (ADINS)

4.5 Analysis of the plan's feasibility

For the satisfactory execution of this project, the direct participation of the HIAS Psychology Department is necessary, as well as, within HIAS, the partnership with ADINS and the Study Center. In the external context, the support provided by SESA in recognizing these regulations will be relevant

subordinate and complementary to internship practices. Furthermore, it is important to consider that, in the desired scenario, the Psychology Department should foster a closer relationship and partnership with the HEIs. It will therefore be important to agree with them on the documents and procedures established by the Psychology Department for the internship process.

Initially, the project was presented to the team of preceptors at the Psychology Department, who confirmed the need for it and their commitment to its implementation. The team is made up of the coordinating psychologist, who is one of the authors of the project, two preceptor psychologists and two care psychologists who have also made their contributions.

The Study Center, as the administrative unit responsible for teaching and research activities at HIAS, should provide institutional support for the project, in the sense of recognizing it and authorizing its execution and subsequent adoption of the procedures for setting up internships in Psychology. The Psychology Department has been in constant contact and dialogue with this unit and has been very accepting of the internship management strategies that have been used so far.

The coordinating psychologist has been trained in the development of standard operating procedures and has already developed the SOPs for the psychology service's assistance actions. However, guidance from ADINS will be necessary for the development of the procedures envisaged in this project. It is envisaged that this office will be able to provide guidance to all the psychologists involved in the process, as has already been positively signaled. ADINS will also be responsible for validating the procedures developed.

In an external scenario in which there is greater demand than supply, the Psychology Department will have to make agreements and negotiate in order to gain recognition for the process of systematizing internships, working to ensure that it is received positively in the midst of existing partnerships and institutional relations. This action requires skill and credibility, but these qualities are already practiced with the HEIs in the administration of the current situation, and so far there have been satisfactory results, even when dealing with cases of disputes and competition for spaces and vacancies. The nod to standardization refers to fairness, equity and transparency, factors that contribute to the acceptance of the project's products.

The logistical resources mentioned in topic 4 are low-cost and do not need to be purchased, as they are already available. The human resources are positively committed and have the time to do so, within a rationally prepared plan. Furthermore, the partnerships at HIAS are designed with acceptance and participation, which constitutes a scenario with far more strengths than weaknesses. There are no antagonistic forces or political issues that could interfere negatively, since the professions enjoy the autonomy they need to make decisions about internships in their areas, as long as they respect the hierarchically established rules, which is the case with this project. Finally, the proposal to overcome a position of vagueness and alternation by offering a regular and homogeneous process, projects a positive organizational scenario.

BIBLIOGRAPHY

BERNARDES, J. S. Psychology education after 50 years of the First National Psychology Curriculum: some current challenges. **Psicol. cienc. prof.**, Brasilia, v. 32, n. spe, 2012 .

BORGES, J. C. S. **Caring for lives: a** historical review of the Albert Sabin Children's Hospital. Fortaleza: HIAS, 2006. 112p.

BRAZIL. Chamber of Deputies. Document and Information Center. Law No. 4.**119 of August 27, 1962.** Provides for degree courses in psychology and regulates the profession of psychologist. Cole^áo de Leis do Brasil - 1962, Page 96 Vol. 5 (Published Original). Available at: < http://www2.camara.leg.br/legin/fed/lei/1960-1969/lei-4119-27-agosto-1962-353841- norma-pl.html >. Accessed on: May 13, 2013.

BRAZIL. Presidency of the Republic. Civil House. **Law No. 6.494 of December 7, 1977.** Provides for internships for students at higher education establishments and 2nd level vocational and supplementary education establishments, and makes other provisions.
Available at: <http://www.planalto.gov.br/ccivil 03/leis/l6494.htm> Accessed on: May 25, 2013.

BRAZIL. Ministry of Health. Executive Secretariat. **Unified Health System (SUS): principles and achievements.** Brasilia: Ministry of Health, 2000.

BRAZIL. MINISTRY OF EDUCATION. **National Curricular Guidelines for Degree Courses in Psychology.** Resolution No. 8, of May 7, 2004. Official Journal of the Union. Brasilia, 2004.

BRAZIL. Ministry of Health. Health Care Secretariat. **Ordinance No. 741, of December 19, 2005.** Defines the parameters for planning and evaluating the high complexity oncology network. Brasilia, 2005. Available at: <http://www.brasilsus.com. br/legislacoes/sas/3501-741>. Accessed on: May 13, 2013.

CARVALHO, B.G.; MARTIN, G.B.; CORDONI, L. The organization of the health system in Brazil. In: ANDRADE, S.M.; SOARES, D.A.; CORDONI, L. **Bases da saúde coletiva. Londrina:** Ed. UEL, 2001, p.27-59.

CEARÁ. Health Department. **Ordinance No. 747/2008 of June 2, 2008.**
Suspends the granting of internship requests by the managers of the Hospital and Outpatient Units that are part of the organizational structure of the State Health Department.

CFP. Federal Council of Psychology. **Resolution No. 010/2005 of July 21, 2005.** Approves the Psychologist's Code of Professional Ethics. Available at: < http://site.cfp.org.br/wp-content/uploads/2012/07/codigo etica.pdf >. Accessed on: May 25, 2013.

. Federal Council of Psychology. **Resolugáo n 003/2007 de 12 de fevereiro de 2007** Institui a Consolidado das Resolu^óes do Conselho Federal de Psicologia. Available at: < http://site.cfp.org.br/wp-

content/uploads/2007/02/resolucao2007_3.pdf >. Accessed on: May 25, 2013.

. Federal Council of Psychology. **Resolution No. 13, of September 14, 2007.** Establishes the Consolidated Resolutions on the Professional Title of Specialist in Psychology and sets out the rules and procedures for its registration. Brasilia, 2007. Available at: <http://www.sbph.org.br/uploads/link/resolucao2007 13.pdf?PHPSESSID=6e00603ba 6bec181af08eb5a6a35adc2 > Accessed on: May 13, 2013.

Federal Council of Psychology. **Resolution No. 03, of February 12, 2007.** Institutes the Consolidation of Resolutions of the Federal Council of Psychology. Brasilia, 2007. Available at: < http://site.cfp.org.br/wp-content/uploads/2003/06/resolucao2003 7.pdf>. Accessed on: May 13, 2013.

. Federal Council of Psychology. **Resolution No. 001/2009 of March 30, 2009.** Establishes the obligation to record documents resulting from the provision of psychological services. Available at:

<http://site.cfp.org.br/wp- content/uploads/2009/04/resolucao2009 01 .pdf>. Accessed on: May 25, 2013.
FREIRE, Paulo. **The importance of the act of reading**. Sao Paulo: Cortez/Autores Associados, 1982. P.
22.)

FREIRE, P. **Pedagogía do oprimido**. 13. ed. Rio de Janeiro: Paz e Terra, 1983.

HIAS. Albert Sabin Children's Hospital. Study Center. **Get to know HIAS**: profile of the Albert Sabin
Children's Hospital - Survey. Fortaleza, 2012.

MARCHIORI, L. M.; MELO, J.; MELO, W. J. Teacher evaluation in relation to new technologies for
didactics and attention in higher education. Avaliagao (Campinas), Sorocaba, v. 16, n. 2, July 2011.

SPINK, M. J. P; MATTA, G. C. Psy professional practice in public health: historical configurations and
contemporary challenges. In: SPINK, M. J. P. (Org). **A psicologia em diálogo com o SUS: prática
profissional e produgao académica**: Sao Paulo, 2007, p. 25 - 52.

APPENDICES

APPENDIX A - GROVE SPREADSHEET

Initial problem question: "Incompatibility between academic training (theoretical) and the real needs of the SUS (practical)"

PA application scenario: Albert Sabin Children's Hospital (HIAS) - Medical Unit Psychology

Target audience: Psychology undergraduates.

Current problem question: "Deficiency in systematizing the process of inserting psychology students into the graduate internship in a tertiary hospital."

APPLICATION PROJECT GROVE SPREADSHEET

Prioritized problem - Deficiency in systematizing the process of inserting psychology students into their graduate internship at a tertiary hospital.

Team/Resources Tackling Objectives

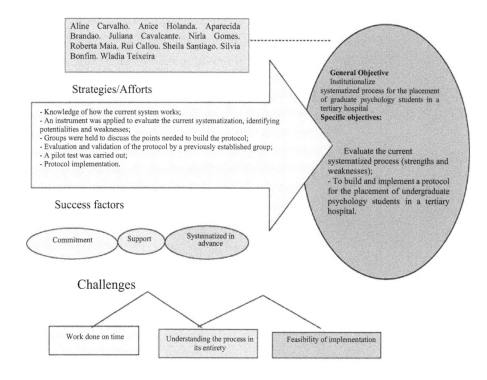

Psychological Assistance for Hospitalized Children Course
Organization: CPC Psychology Unit and NOEL/NAIF - HOSPITAL INFANTIL ALBERT SABIN
PARTNERSHIP AND SUPPORT: ASSOCIAÇÃO PETER PAN
Syllabus for semester 2013.1

DATE	TIME	CONTENTS	TEACHER	HOURS
FRIDAY 12.04.2013				
MORNING	08h-10h	Early childhood syndromes: epidemiology and main types	Erlane Ribeiro (HIAS)	2h/a
	10am-10:30pm	Interval		
	10:30am-12:30pm	Child and adolescent cancer: epidemiology, main types of tumors and treatment	Atur Moraes (HIAS-CPC)	2h/a
AFTERNOON	2pm-4pm	Health Psychology in the hospital context in Public Health.	Cinthia Vasconcelos (HC - Porto Alegre)	2h/a
	16h-16:30h	Interval		
	16:30h-18:30h	Theoretical-methodological framework and strategies for psychological care for hospitalized children.	Anice Holanda (CPC)	2h/a
SATURDAY 13.04.2013	**TIME**	**CONTENTS**	**TEACHER**	**HOURS**
MORNING	08h-10h	Psychoeducation in the pediatric hospital setting.	Daniele Furlani (UNIFOR)	2h/a
	10am-10:30pm	Interval		
	10:30am-12:00pm	Psychological assessment - application to the pediatric hospital context.	Mércia Capistrano (FCRS)	2h/a

TIME	CONTENTS	TEACHER	HOURS
FRIDAY 19.04.2013			
MORNING 08h-10h	Brief Focal Psychotherapy - Brief Supportive Psychotherapy.	Regina Celi (NOEL/NAIF)	2h/a
10am-10:30pm	Interval		
10:30am-12:30pm	Palliative Care in Pediatric Oncology	Giselle Sucupira (UNIFOR)	2h/a
AFTERNOON 2pm-4pm	The Humanization Policy and Hospital Psychology	Harrismana Pinto (CPC)	2h/a
16h-16:30h	Interval		
16:30h-18:30h	Registration of psychological interventions and Guardianship in the Hospital Context.	Anice Holanda (CPC)	2h/a
SATURDAY 20.04.2013			
TIME	CONTENTS	TEACHER	HOURS
MORNING 08h-09:15h	Multiprofessional team and interdisciplinary work - Experience in Palliative Care.	Fernanda Gomes (APP-CPC)	1:15h
09:15-09:30	Interval		
09:30-10:45	The Peter Pan Association - Volunteering and the Support Network for patients and their families.	Olga Maia (APP)	1:15h
10:45am -12pm	Social Work in Pediatric Oncology and working in partnership with the Psychology team.	Socorro Alencar (CPC)	1:15h
TOTAL WORKLOAD			
TIME	CONTENTS	HOURS	
		24h/a	

ANNEX B

PROCEDURES AND GUIDELINES FOR PSYCHOLOGY ACTIVITIES

REFERENCE: 2013-1
Intervention units:
1. Nursery (3rd floor)
2. Chemotherapy-Day (QT-DIA) and Outpatient Clinics (1st floor)
3. Procedures Unit (2nd floor)
4. Sequential Chemotherapy (QTS) (2nd floor)
5. Intensive Care Unit (CPC ICU) (2nd floor)

OBS: Psychology room: first and second floor.

CPC - Important figures:

Units/Programs/Volunteers.	Quantitative
Outpatient clinics:	
Early Diagnosis	01
Nutrition	01
Treatment	04
Palliative care	01
Number of users per day	70
Day Hospital beds:	16
Sequential chemotherapy beds:	24
In-house beds:	24
I.T.U. beds	07
APP's social programs and projects	20
Number of volunteers	217

Activities carried out by Psychology:

Assistance:
Position: Nursing (E)

Activities:

1. **Individual/dyadic care for hospitalized patients and companions:**
   a. Access the daily patient map, available on the Psychology computers (my computer/psychologycpcem serverhias/technical folder/registration map/ folder daily patient map/ daily map 2013/ folder month - see date).
   b. Updating the nursing census (third floor station), identifying new arrivals, patients with complications, patients in relapse and palliative care patients.
   c. If follow-up is available for all patients, it should be carried out; if not, triage should be carried out with the following priorities: 1) emergencies; 2) newcomers; 3) requests from the team and/or family members, relapse patients and patients who cannot be cured.

   d. In the case of triage, an anamnesis should be taken (with newcomers) and oriented towards this type of patient and the others.
   e. Individual, dyad or dyad care, at the bedside, in the psychology room or elsewhere in the ward.
   f. Inter-consultation and coordination with the pediatric oncology team and APP's social programs;
   g. Technical reference: Brief focal psychotherapy, Counseling
      Psychological (or other as agreed in the intervention project)
   h. Use of play materials, which must be aseptically cleaned at the end.
   i. Monday to Friday and/or Saturday

j.   Registration in accordance with CFP resolution 001/2009.

k.   File the play product (drawings, paintings) in an A-Z folder, in alphabetical order, putting the patient's full name and date on the drawing.

FLOWCHART:

1) NEW PATIENT:
    a. In full care: ATTENDANCE/ANAMNESIS - CONTRACT - FOLLOW-UP IN THE NURSERY, ICU AND AMBULATORY FOLLOW-UP, if applicable (for closure) - EVALUATION - DISCHARGE - REFERRAL TO THE PSYCHOLOGY TEAM OF THE SEQUENTIAL DAY/QT HOSPITAL;
    b. On a triage basis: ATTENDANCE/ANAMNESIS - REFERENCE GUIDELINES FOR NURSING PSYCHOLOGY TEAMS and/or SEQUENTIAL DAY-HOSPITAL/QT;

2) NON-NOVICE PATIENT:
    a. CARE - CONTRACT - FOLLOW-UP IN THE NURSERY, ICU, SUPPORT OUTPATIENT AND OUTPATIENT FOLLOW-UP (for closure) - EVALUATION - DISCHARGE/COBIT - REFERRAL TO THE PSYCHOLOGY TEAM OF THE SEQUENTIAL DAY/QT HOSPITAL;
    b. On a triage basis: ATTENDANCE - GUIDANCE- REFERRAL FOR NURSING PSYCHOLOGY TEAM and/or SEQUENTIAL DAY-HOSPITAL/QT;

Allocation: I.T.U. (ICU)

Activities:

1. **Individual care/follow-up dyad by the member of the psychology team who has been attending the ward or Day Hospital/Sequential QT:**

    a. Access the daily patient map, available on the Psychology computers (my computer/psychologycpcem serverhias/technical folder/registration map/ folder daily patient map/ daily map 2013/ folder month - see date).

    b. Care psychologist Harris acts as a reference in the I.T.U. The trainee should receive guidance from her on the specifics of the sector.

    c. Carrying out active searches in the I.T.U. using the nursing census, identifying new arrivals, complications and palliative care patients.

    d. Individual/dyadic care at the bedside and/or in the psychology room or in another area of the ICU anteroom in the case of companions.

    e. Technical reference: brief focal psychotherapy, psychological counseling (or other agreed upon in the intervention project).

    f. Interconsultation and coordination with APP's team and social programs;

    g. Use of play materials that are possible and authorized in the ITU, with proper asepsis.

    h. Monday to Friday and/or Saturday

    i. Registration in accordance with CFP resolution 001/2009.

    j. File the play product (drawings, paintings) in an A-Z folder, in alphabetical order, putting the patient's full name and date on the drawing.

FLOWCHART:
1) NEW PATIENT:
    a. ATTENDANCE/ANAMNESIS - CONTRACT - FOLLOW-UP IN THE NURSERY AND AMBULATORY FOLLOW-UP (for closure, if applicable) - EVALUATION - DISCHARGE/COBIT - REFERRAL TO THE DAY-HOSPITAL PSYCHOLOGY TEAM/SEQUENTIAL QT;

2) NON-NOVICE PATIENT:

a. CARE - CONTRACT - FOLLOW-UP IN NURSING, SUPPORT OUTPATIENT AND OUTPATIENT FOLLOW-UP (for closure) - EVALUATION - DISCHARGE/OBIT - REFERRAL TO SEQUENTIAL DAY-HOSPITAL/QT PSYCHOLOGY TEAM;

2. **Carrying out orientation and support work for companions transferred to the ICU and visiting family members, including individual/dyadic care for the latter if necessary.**
   a. Orientation sessions held in the afternoon or evening before visiting hours, in the I.T.U. waiting room;
   b. Individual/dyad care for emergency cases, if necessary.
   c. Support during visiting hours and in communication with the intensive care team, with the aim of mediating the family-team relationship.
   d. Technical reference: Brief focal psychotherapy, Counseling Psychological (or other agreed in the intervention project)
   e. Use of graphic materials and multimedia resources.
   f. Monday to Friday and/or Saturday/Sunday.
   g. Registration in accordance with CFP resolution 001/2009.

CAPACITY: SEQUENTIAL QTY (QTS)

Activities:

1. **Attendance for patients and companions in a semi-interment regime:**

   8. Access the daily patient map, available on the Psychology computers (my computer/psicologiacpcem servidorhias/technical folder/registration map/ folder daily patient map/ daily map 2013/ folder month - see date.

   9. Visits to beds; consultation of medical records, with a welcome for all patients;
   10. Psychological assessment of demands using a specific instrument;
   11. The number of consultations given to cases with an identified demand, with psychological listening:
   12. Inter-consultations where necessary and interaction with the team;
   13. Theoretical references: Psychological counseling/ brief supportive psychotherapy (or another agreed upon in the intervention project).
   14. Articulated with volunteers or Occupational Therapists and/or carried out playful interventions with the children/adolescents.
   15. Monday to Friday.
   1. Registration in accordance with CFP resolution 001/2009.
   2. File the play product (drawings, paintings) in an A-Z folder, in alphabetical order, putting the patient's full name and date on the drawing.

3. **Assistance through an orientation and support group for carers:**
   a. An open multi-professional group inviting mothers and other accompanying family members present in the QTS and ICU (due to the proximity of the environment).
   b. Frequency: weekly or fortnightly (depending on the group's availability), Thursday afternoons;
   c. Content aimed at providing information about the disease, treatment, health care and promoting support for psycho-emotional needs, without assuming a psychotherapeutic nature.
   d. Technical reference: support groups, psycho-education, health education.
   e. Use of graphic materials, multimedia resources.
   f. Registration in accordance with CFP resolution 001/2009.

CAPACITY: DAY HOSPITAL (HD)

Activities:

1. **Psychology Outpatient Clinic:**
   a. Patient and/or family care through active search or at the request of family members and/or

staff;

b.   This service is based on an assessment of the complaint and demand, followed by the definition of the appropriate intervention : oriented;

Psychological counseling/BS support; psycho-education, among others (defining referral/follow-up) or focal brief psychotherapy - process or support.

c. Carrying out reception duties to meet the free demands of the children who come to the room, organizing individual or group play activities.

d. Technical reference: Brief Focal Psychotherapy, Counseling Psychological, Health Education, Reception (or another agreed in the intervention project).

e. Interconsultation and coordination with APP's team and social programs;

f. Use of graphic and playful materials.

g. Monday to Friday.

h. Registration in accordance with CFP resolution 001/2009.

i. Record the play product (drawings, paintings) in an A-Z folder, in alphabetical order, putting the patient's full name and date on the drawing.

2. **Early Diagnosis Clinic:**

a. Actively search for cases with a confirmed diagnosis with the nursing technician at the clinic (or other means).

b. Participate in the diagnostic report, if requested by the attending physician.

c. If follow-up is available for all patients, do it.

a. If there aren't any, triage the most critical cases and take anamnesis, welcome and guide them.

b. Individual or dyad care in the psychology room or in another part of the Day Hospital.

c. Interconsultation and coordination with APP's team and social programs;

d. Technical reference: Brief focal psychotherapy, Counseling Psychological.

e. Use of play materials.

f. Monday to Friday.

g. Registration in accordance with CFP resolution 001/2009.

h. File the play product (drawings, paintings) in an A-Z folder, in alphabetical order, putting the patient's full name and date on the drawing.

FLOWCHART:

a. Under the full care regime: ATTENDANCE/ANAMNESIS - CONTRACT - FOLLOW-UP IN THE DAY HOSPITAL, NURSING, ICU AND AMBULATORY FOLLOW-UP (for closure) - EVALUATION - DISCHARGE - REFERRAL TO THE DAY HOSPITAL/SEQUENTIAL QT AND/OR NURSING PSYCHOLOGY TEAM.

b. On a triage basis: ATTENDANCE/ANAMNESIS - RECEPTION/ORIENTATIONS- REFERRAL TO NURSING PSYCHOLOGY TEAM and/or DAY-HOSPITAL/QT

SEQUENTIAL;

3. **Waiting Room Project:**

a. **Diagnostic/Control Procedures Waiting Room (Procedures Unit:**

    i. Welcome

    ii. Identified new and veteran patients

    iii. Playful activities.

    iv. Guidance/support for patients and/or companions about the tests to be carried out and the process of coping with the diagnosis, for newcomers, with the use of a serial album.

    v.Registration on a specific form and in accordance with CFP Resolution 001/2009, remembering to include the full name of the patient and companion.

    vi. Statistical monitoring of informals for scientific papers.

b. **Support Group for Children with Cancer.**
    i. Invitation to patients aged 07 and over
    ii. Free membership
    iii. Semi-structured activity, with themes related to the child development, illness and treatment.
    iv. Use of play materials, graphics and books.
    v. Frequency: two meetings a week.
    vi. Time: approximately one and a half hours. Registration in accordance with CFP resolution 001/2009, remembering to include the patients' full names.

4. **Welcoming Patients and Companions:**
    a. Welcoming patients with a clear suspicion of cancer, strengthening the bond during pre-admission, listening to their doubts and advising them on the importance of **coping with the diagnostic process**;
    b. Welcoming newly diagnosed patients to the ward, informing them about the issues that are most important to them.
    c. The strategy is to welcome the discourses and subjective issues related to the possible diagnosis and actual diagnosis of cancer and to the treatment, evaluate, provide psychological guidance and, if necessary, refer for psychotherapeutic care at the CPC Psychology Unit;
    d. Carry out health education activities based on the autonomy of patients/family members, in other words, work on the points that they consider important for their adaptation when they arrive, using material prepared for this purpose, such as the Educational Booklet for Parents, if it is accepted and it is perceived that this is the strategic moment.
    e. Coordination with the social programs of the A'PP and with Social Services.
    Methodology:
    f. Identify the users present in the newly admitted ward;
    g. Based on the daily numbers, schedule and carry out individual/dyad reception sessions for users with a clear suspicion of cancer and new patients and their companions, using educational materials;
    h. A welcome session and individual guidance for the dyad.

ASSIGNMENT: SUNSHINE PROGRAM - PALLIATIVE CARE (PRS-CP):

A PC care strategy that involves all of the CPC's units, and is based on a multi-professional "support clinic" (doctor, psychologist, nurse and other professionals) aimed at supporting patients who are beyond the point of cure, with an emphasis on pain and palliative care in general. The above-mentioned program is in direct partnership with the psychology program, which is made up of a professor and three extension workers.

Activities:
    a. Participation in the Palliative Care (PC) Meeting, which takes place every Wednesday morning from 8:30 to 9:30 in the psychology room on the second floor, attended by the multi-professional team, the project coordinator, the extension workers, one or more care psychologists and the 20h trainee from the Day Hospital.
    b. The assistant members of the psychology team will be the reference for the multi-professional team and the PRS-CP in terms of palliative care.
    c. Once the phase beyond the possibility of cure has been communicated, care will be extended through the PRS-CP. This expansion and introduction of the PRS-CP team will be done by the psychology assistant, introducing and fostering the bond with this new member.
    d. Once this has been done, a unique therapeutic project (PTS) will be drawn up by the psychology assistant, a member of the PRS-CP and other professionals from the support team/ambulatory. A member of the PRS-CP will take over the case and will be able to take part in the communication session about the out-of-cure situation and other interventions.
    e. Through the PT, when necessary, coordination with the cancer care network should be encouraged and carried out.
    f. The member of the PRS-CP will contribute to the extension of care through strategies for extending care to family members, home visits, making dreams come true and other actions.

g. Interconsultation/discussion/ongoing support with the APP team and programs will be provided by those who conduct the PTS of patients undergoing PC.
h. Registration in accordance with CFP resolution 001/2009
i. Record the play production (drawings, paintings) in an A-Z folder, in alphabetical order, putting the patient's full name and date on the drawing.

Teaching and Research (EP):
Allocation: Núcleo Mais Vida - NMV and participation in the Albert Sabin Children's Hospital Study Center - HIAS

1. Carrying out and/or participating in research activities developed by the NMV and/or the HIAS Study Center, involving the collection, transcription, analysis, discussion and preparation of scientific papers.
2. Carried out and/or participated in extension and teaching activities of the NMV and/or HAIS Study Center, involving elaboration, carrying out of programs and/or projects and events aimed at the internal public of the CPC and the community.
3. Participated in special NMV/APP projects. Current projects:
   a. Care Network with the NASF - continued actions (reception with delivery of the educational booklet and support group for parents and insertion of other activities)
   b. Early Diagnosis Program - Quixadá and Quixeramobim (start: June)

Coordination (CO):

Location: Psychology Coordination (there is no specific room, it can be in the CPC and/or the NMV)
1. Design and execution of introductory training for trainees, extension workers and volunteers.
2. Supervision of the activities carried out by trainees and extension workers, through systematic monitoring and weekly/fortnightly meetings for technical supervision, and study and discussion groups.
3. Management of the process of attracting trainees and extension workers, involving participation in propositional and/or deliberative bodies, preparation and monitoring of the relevant documents, interaction with the various players in the process in order to resolve the referrals.
4. Management of the course of the internship and extension projects, involving participation in propositional and/or deliberative bodies, preparation and monitoring of the relevant documents, interaction with the various players in the process to resolve any issues.
5. Management of the research and extension activities of the NMV and/or HIAS Study Center under the responsibility of Psychology, involving the monitoring of scholarship holders, trainees or extension workers and external researchers who work directly with research.
6. Management of the administrative and logistical process of the Psychology Unit of the CPC, involving actions relating to human resources, acquisition and maintenance of material, furniture, physical structure and other pertinent actions, including the provision of pertinent documentation and its follow-up.
7. Management of the work process of psychology as part of a multi-professional team, involving the planning of programs, projects and projects, monitoring them, resolving conflicts and obstacles, participating in propositional and deliberative bodies and other appropriate actions, including providing the relevant documentation and monitoring it.
8. Collaborated with the JPA on matters for which it was called upon, including the design   , preparation, execution and/or monitoring of programs,
   projects, memberships, administrative actions, attracting and training volunteers, among others.
9. Informal coordination of Psychology at HIAS, involving actions relating to all of the above.

10. Represented Psychology on the HIAS Human Research Ethics Committee, Bioethics Committee and Editorial Board of HIAS journals.

INDIVIDUAL CARE / THE DYAD
TYPES OF PSYCHOLOGICAL CARE

SIGLA	PROCEDURE NAME
APRD	Pre-diagnostic care
APD	Post-diagnostic care
API	Psychological Intercourse
AE	Emergency services
ARC	Relapse care
AFPC	Out-of-Possibility-of-Cure Care
APO	Post-death family care
APC	Surgery Preparation Care
OP	Psychological guidance
VP	Psychological visit
ITC	Professional Interconsultation
OAP	Other Psychological Care Not Described

SERVICES/PRODUCTS	DESCRIPTION
Hospital, outpatient and home support services.	JCoutpatient medical consultations in the following specialties: cardiology, oncology, hepatology, dermatology, endocrinology, gastroenterology, genetics, allergology, hematology, infectology, nephrology, neurology, ophthalmology, orthopedics, neurosurgery, pulmonology, rheumatology, neonatology, otorhinolaryngology, gynecology for children and adolescents, psychiatry and pediatric surgery in 8 specialties, J ConsultaseAtendimentosEspecializadosem : Psychology, nursing, nutrition, speech therapy, dentistry, physiotherapy, occupational therapy, psychopedagogy and social assistance. J **Emergency care in:** pediatric clinic and surgery. J l **nternagöes hospital:** Clinical, surgical, specialty pediatrics, pediatric and neonatal intensive care. J l **home hospitalizations,** including patients on invasive mechanical ventilation. J **Hospitaldia in:** oncology, nephrology ,genetics, immunology, rheumatology, pulmonology and cystic fibrosis. J **Support services:** clinical pathology laboratory, microbiology, immunohistochemistry, molecular biology , cytogenetics, diagnostic imaging, graphic methods, audiometry, pharmacy, dentistry, occupational therapy, speech therapy , nursing, physiotherapy, psychology, psycho-pedagogy, social services, nutrition and dietetics, parenteral and enteral nutrition, the Medical Archive and Statistics Sector (SAME), the Sterile Material Center (CME), the Hospital Medical Material Center (CMMH), the Hospital Infectious Diseases Control Committee (CCIH), the ombudsman's office, Specialized Service for Safety and Occupational Medicine (SESMT), Internal Accident Prevention Committee (CIPA), Hospital Health Risk Management (GRSH), milk bank, kangaroo project, epidemiology, immunization with CRIE (Reference Center for Special Immunobiologicals), neonatal screening, Center for the Prevention of Infectious Diseases (Núcleo de

	Evaluation of Health Technology (NATS), Internal Regulatory Center. *J* **Hospitality and Administrative Support Services**: Corrective and preventive building and equipment maintenance, general services, purchasing management, warehouse, accounting, cost center, quality office, materials and assets, personnel sector, human development service, art workshop, GRSS (Health Service Waste Management), linen, transport, equipment center, information technology sector, social services.
Teaching and Research	**JMedical** *residency*: pediatric surgery, orthopedics, general pediatrics and cardiology , cancer and pulmonology, hematology, neonatology, nephrology, gastroenterology, intensive care. J 1 **nternship:** medicine and nursing, J **Curricular internships** in nursing, physiotherapy, psychology, social work, dentistry, pharmacy J **Research projects** approved by the local ethics committee. J **Organized scientific technical events.**

NON-COMPULSORY INTERNSHIP FORM

NAME: **PHONE NUMBERS:**

STREET (AVENUE):   N°

COMPLEMENT: **CITY:**   **STATE:**   **ZIP CODE:**

E-mail: UNIVERSITY OF ORIGIN - UFC ( ) - UNIFOR( ) - FATECI (   )

- UECE (   ) - OTHER (   ):

1.   **PREFERENTIAL /REFENTIAL THEORETICAL APPROACH (the one you've been studying/training the most):**

2.   **COMPULSORY (CURRICULAR) AND/OR NON-COMPULSORY (EXTRA-CURRICULAR) PRACTICAL EXPERIENCE IN THE CLINICAL AND HOSPITAL/HEALTH AREAS (PREFERABLY INTERNSHIP). If you do not have experience in these areas, please mention institutional areas, if any: SOCIAL, LEGAL, SCHOOL-EDUCATIONAL AND OTHER.**

CLIENT AGE GROUP: (   ) changas ( )adolescents ()   adults

(   )senior citizens

TYPE OF EXPERIENCE(S):

INTERVENTION MODALITY(IES) PREDOMINANT IN ALL THE EXPERIMENTS:

(   ) individual ( )group ( )family ( )community ( )other:

3.   **HIS ACADEMIC TRAINING, UNTIL NOW, HAS FOCUSED ON:**

( )Clinical Psychology ( )Hospital/Health Psychology ( )Community Social Psychology ( )   Legal Psychology ( )Educational Psychology

( )Organizational and Work Psychology   ( )other.

4.   **THEORETICAL TRAINING IN CLINICAL PSYCHOLOGY (courses, study groups / courses / scientific events, of short or medium duration or training courses / long duration):**

(   ) yes. Cite the one with the highest workload:

(   ) no

5.   **THEORETICAL CAPACITY BUILDING IN HOSPITAL PSYCHOLOGY/HEALTH PSYCHOLOGY (courses, study groups/courses/scientific events, of short or medium duration or training/long-term courses):**

(   ) yes. Cite the one with the highest workload:

(   ) no

6. THEORETICAL CAPACITY BUILDING IN PSYCHOLOGY (courses, study groups / courses / scientific events, of short or medium duration or training courses / long duration):

(   ) yes. Cite the one with the highest workload:

(   ) no

7. THEORETICAL CAPACITY BUILDING IN BRIEF FOCAL PSYCHOTHERAPY (courses, study groups / courses / scientific events, of short or medium duration or training courses / long duration):

(   ) yes. Name the course with the most hours: psychological counseling:

(   ) no

16. DO YOU **ONLY STUDY?** (   ) **YES** (   ) **NO**. Other activity(ies) performed(s):

HOW MANY SUBJECTS WILL YOU TAKE IN THE SEMESTER IN WHICH THE INTERNSHIP BEGINS?
HOW MANY OTHER INTERNSHIPS IN THE SAME SEMESTER?

9. PSYCHOTHERAPY:

(   ) currently does ( ) has done (   )never done

10. AVAILABLE HOURS FOR THE INTERNSHIP:

MARK WITH AN **X**

TIME	SEG	TER	WEDNESDAY	QUIN	FRIDAY	OBSERVATIONS:
8-9						
9-10						
10-11						
11-12						
13-14						
14-15						
15-16						
16-17						
17-18						

Milton Keynes UK
Ingram Content Group UK Ltd.
UKHW040110160324
439374UK00001B/99